LOTS TO SPOT

DANGEROUS DINOSAURS

Matthew Scott

ARCTURUS

ARCTURUS

This edition published in 2019 by Arcturus Publishing Limited
26/27 Bickels Yard, 151–153 Bermondsey Street,
London SE1 3HA

Copyright © Arcturus Holdings Limited

Edited by Susannah Bailey
Written by William Potter
Illustrated by Matthew Scott
Designed by Trudi Webb

ISBN: 978-1-78950-298-5
CH006687NT
Supplier 33, Date 0119, Print run 8073

Printed in China

CONTENTS

Tanystropheus
(tan-ee-STROFE-ee-us)
Tanystropheus was a long-necked reptile that could dip its head into water to catch fish.

Find 5

Find 5

Mastodonsaurus
(MAS-toe-don-sore-us)
This huge, frog-like creature was the largest known amphibian.

BEACH BEASTS

225 million years ago, the first dinosaurs appeared. The Earth was very hot, with no ice at the North and South Poles.

Liliensternus
(lil-ee-en-STERN-us)
The largest land predator of its day, it had a jaw full of sharp teeth.

Find 5

Find 5

Plateosaurus
(PLAT-ee-o-sore-us)
This dinosaur could stand on its back legs to reach tree leaves.

Find 3

Gerrothorax
(jeh-row-THORE-ax)
Gerrothorax was a flat creature, like a giant tadpole, which lived in and out of water.

Find 5

Placochelys
(plack-oh-KELL-iss)
Placochelys was one of the earliest known turtles, with a flat, knobbly shell.

Find 5

Saltopus
(SALT-o-puss)
This meat-eating dino walked on two legs and was the size of a cat.

Find 2

Ruehleia
(roo-LAY-ah)
An early sauropod, Ruehleia had a small head and a long neck and tail.

Find 5

Procompsognathus
(pro-comp-SOG-nay-thus)
This small, fast hunter would have eaten insects and lizards.

Find 6

Thecodontosaurus
(THEE-co-DON-toh-sore-us)
A skinny, plant-eating dino, it hid in caves when threatened.

5

Centrosaurus
(SEN-tro-sore-us)
Centrosaurus was a horned, plant-eating dinosaur that lived in a large herd.

Find 5

Pachyrhinosaurus
(PAK-ee-rye-no-SORE-us)
This elephant-sized dinosaur had a horned plate protecting its head.

Find 4

STAMPEDE!

It's 75 million years ago and a hungry Albertosaurus is on the hunt.
Run for your life!

Corythosaurus
(ko-RITH-uh-sore-us)
These dinos called to each other with loud, trumpet-like noises.

Find 8

Find 6

Atrociraptor
(a-TRO-see-rap-tor)
This small raptor would be only a snack for Albertosaurus!

Find 5

Prosaurolophus
(pro-SORE-rol-uh-fus)
The plant-eating Prosaurolophus had a mouth like a duck's bill.

Find 5 ← **Edmontonia**
(ed-mon-TOE-nia)
This plant-eater was built like a tank, with spikes all over its back.

Find 7 ←
Pachycephalosaurus
(pak-ee-SEF-ul-lo-sore-us)
Pachycephalosaurus had a domed, spiky skull it could use for head-butting.

Find 5 ←
Lambeosaurus
(LAM-be-uh-sore-us)
A giant plant-eater, Lambeosaurus had two head crests and pebbly skin.

Euoplocephalus
(you-op-luh-SEF-uh-lus)
These dinos had hammer-like, clubbed tails they could swing.

Find 1 → **Albertosaurus**
(al-BERT-oh-sore-us)
This fast predator hunted eight million years before T. rex.

Find 3 ←

Brachiosaurus
(BRACK-ee-uh-sore us)
This dino was so large, an adult human could only reach its knee.

Find 3

Hesperosaurus
(hes-PARE-uh-sore-us)
A plant-eater with round plates on its back, Hesperosaurus used its tail to defend itself.

Find 3

GRAZING GIANTS

The late Jurassic was a time of giant, long-necked sauropods that ate from the tallest trees.

Apatosaurus
(ah-PAT-uh-sore-us)
Like all sauropods, Apatosaurus ate plants, such as conifers and ferns.

Find 3

Find 5

Dryosaurus
(DRY-o-sore-us)
This ostrich-sized dino lived on leaves. Its name means "tree lizard."

Find 3

Allosaurus
(AL-oh-sore-us)
Allosaurus was the biggest meat-eater in North America.

Find 3

Camarasaurus
(kuh-MARE-uh-sore-us)
A sauropod with a shorter neck
than others, it ate plants near the ground.

Find 3

Gargoyleosaurus
(gar-GOYL-ee-oh-sore-us)
This dinosaur's spiky back
protected it from attack.

Find 3

Stegosaurus
(STEG-uh-SORE-us)
Stegosaurus had diamond-shaped
plates along its back and a spiked tail.

Camptosaurus
(CAMP-tuh-sore-us)
This plant-eating dinosaur
walked on two legs.

Find 4

Find 3

Diplodocus
(di-plo-DO-kus)
Although Dippy was one of the
longest land animals, it had one
of the smallest brains.

9

Thescelosaurus
(THES-kel-oh-sore-us)
This plant-eating dinosaur
was about as tall as a cow.

Find 13

Find 8

Champsosaurus
(CHAMP-soh-sore-us)
Champsosaurus was a reptile that
caught fish in its long, narrow jaws.

SWAMP DWELLERS

Welcome to the swamp! Many
different kinds of dinosaurs hunted
and grazed here, alongside
other prehistoric creatures.

Albertosaurus
(al-BERT-oh-sore-us)
Albertosaurus, a fierce predator, could
run very fast on its strong back legs.

Find 4

Find 5

Adocus
(ah-DOH-kus)
This ancient reptile looked
a lot like today's turtles.

Find 3

Puertasaurus
(PWUHR-tah-sore-us)
Puertasaurus was as long as
three double-decker buses!

Find 4

Triceratops
(try-SEH-rah-tops)
Triceratops used its huge horns
to fight off fierce predators!

Find 8

Pteranodon
(tuh-RAN-oh-don)
Pteranodon, a flying reptile,
had a crest on its head.

Find 5

Edmontosaurus
(ED-mon-toe-sore-us)
This duck-billed dinosaur lived in
large groups and ate plants.

Anzu
(AN-zoo)
Anzu was a bird-like dinosaur,
with feathers, claws, and a beak!

Find 7

Find 3

Ankylosaurus
(AN-kih-loh-sore-us)
A plant-eating dinosaur that
had a club at the end of its tail.

Hylaeosaurus
(HIGH-lee-oh-sore-us)
Hylaeosaurus, a plant-eater, was one of
the first dinosaurs to be discovered.

Find 4

Eotyrannus
(ee-oh-ti-RAN-us)
Eotyrannus, a small raptor, was
an early relative of T. rex.

Find 3

FLOODLAND FEAST

125 million years ago, the sea levels
rose and forests around the coasts
became flooded.

Pelorosaurus
(pel-oh-ROW-sore-us)
This long-necked sauropod ate tough
plants with its super-strong teeth.

Find 3

Find 3

Baryonyx
(bare-ee-ON-ix)
These dinos might have used
their long claws to spear fish.

Find 7

Hypsilophodon
(hip-sih-LO-fuh-don)
Hypsilophodon, a fast plant-eater,
was the size of a large dog.

12

Find 3

Becklespinax
(beck-el-SPIEN-ax)
This meat-eating dinosaur would
have hunted Pelorosaurus.

Find 5

Iguanodon
(ig-WAN-oh-don)
The fern-eating Iguanodon was one of
the first dinosaurs to be given a name.

Find 5

Neovenator
(nee-oh-ve-NAY-tor)
A small and fast raptor, it was
a threat to Iguanodon.

Valdosaurus
(VAL-doe-sore-us)
The name of this small
dinosaur means "forest lizard."

Find 4

Polacanthus
(pol-a-KAN-thus)
This plant-eating dinosaur
had rows of spikes along its back.

Find 8

13

Troodon young
(TRO-uh-don)
Hatchlings had tiny feathers,
just like their parents.

Find 9

Troodon
(TRO-uh-don)
Troodon was a goose-like dinosaur
that sat on and guarded a
nest of up to 24 eggs.

Find 2

BABY BITERS

Baby dinosaurs were born from eggs. The
parents sometimes protected their nests
from hungry visitors.

Parasaurolophus
(par-ah-sore-OL-uh-fus)
The crest on this dino's head was
a long, hollow tube.

Find 4

Find 5

Dragonflies
Prehistoric dragonflies were much
bigger than today's insects.

Find 3

Edmontosaurus
(ed-MON-tuh-sore-us)
This plant-eating dinosaur had about
1,000 diamond-shaped teeth.

14

Find 3

Panoplosaurus
(pan-OP-lur-sore-us)
Panoplosaurus was protected by a
tough back and spikes on its shoulders.

Find 6

Brachychamsa
(brack-ee-CHAM-sa)
This early alligator lurked in the
water, eyeing the hatchlings hungrily.

Find 6

Hadrosaurus
(HAD-ruh-sore-us)
Hadrosaurus dug hollows in
the ground to make nests.

Helopanoplia
(hell-o-pan-OP-li-a)
This early turtle lived
mostly in the water.

Find 4

Find 3

Triceratops
(try-SAIR-uh-tops)
A bulky dinosaur that weighed the
same as two African elephants.

Pterodactylus
(ter-oh-DAK-til-us)
Pterodactylus had wings made of skin stretched between its arms and legs.

Gnathosaurus
(NATH-oh-sore-us)
This pterosaur had a spoon-shaped beak and teeth as sharp as needles.

Find 6

Find 6

FLYING HIGH

150 million years ago, large reptiles called pterosaurs ruled the skies, along with the first birds.

Anurognathus
(an-YOOR-og-NATH-us)
Anurognathus, a small, flying creature, fed on insects such as damselflies.

Find 5

Find 1

Dakosaurus
(DACK-oh-sore-us)
Dakosaurus, a huge, toothy sea monster, was related to the crocodile.

Find 6

Aerodactylus
(AIR-oh-DAK-til-us)
This duck-sized pterosaur was named after a Pokémon character.

Find 6

Scaphognathus
(sca-fog-NAYTH-us)
Scaphognathus had a long tail
and a bony crest on its head.

Find 5

Rhamphorhynchus
(RAM-for-INK-us)
This pterosaur scooped up fish
with its curved beak full of teeth.

Find 8

Dimorphodon
(di-MORF-oh-don)
Dimorphodon was a large-headed pterosaur
that hunted small prey, including insects.

Archaeopteryx
(ar-kee-OP-ter-ix)
This early bird was the size of a pigeon,
and had claws on its wings.

Find 4

Find 9

Libellulium
(li-bel-LUL-ium)
The prehistoric dragonfly,
Libellulium, was as big as a sparrow.

17

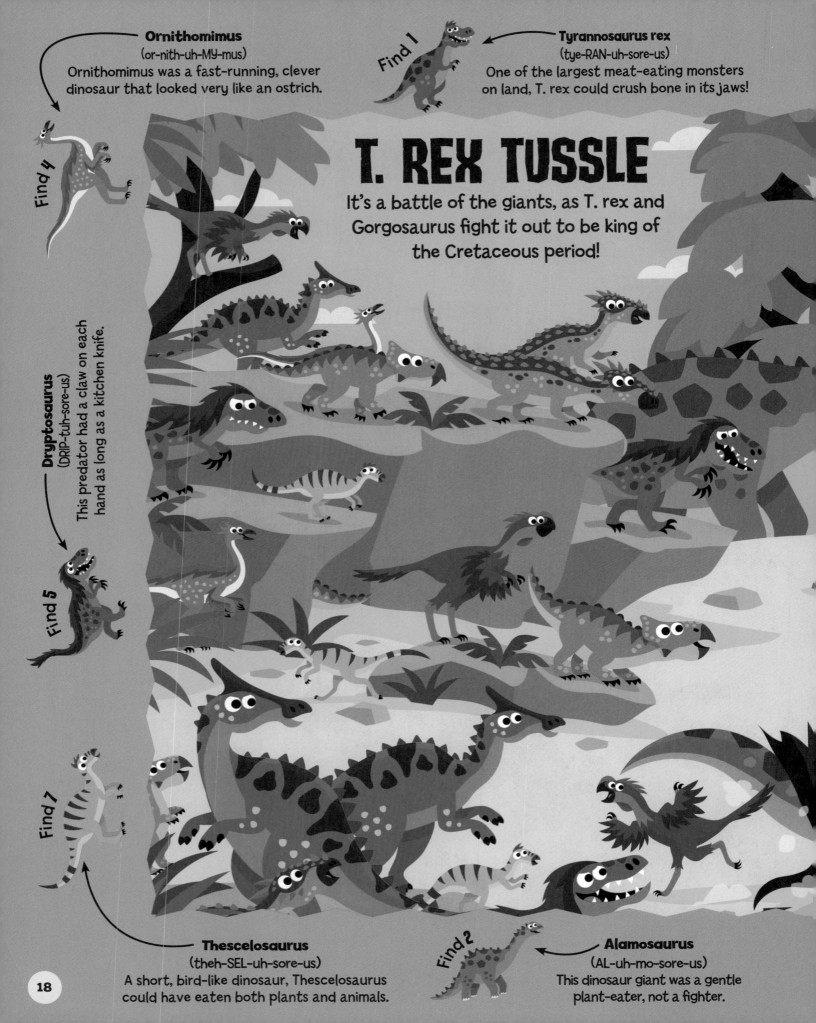

Ornithomimus
(or-nith-uh-MY-mus)
Ornithomimus was a fast-running, clever dinosaur that looked very like an ostrich.

Find 1

Tyrannosaurus rex
(tye-RAN-uh-sore-us)
One of the largest meat-eating monsters on land, T. rex could crush bone in its jaws!

T. REX TUSSLE

It's a battle of the giants, as T. rex and Gorgosaurus fight it out to be king of the Cretaceous period!

Find 4

Dryptosaurus
(DRIP-tuh-sore-us)
This predator had a claw on each hand as long as a kitchen knife.

Find 5

Find 7

Thescelosaurus
(theh-SEL-uh-sore-us)
A short, bird-like dinosaur, Thescelosaurus could have eaten both plants and animals.

Find 2

Alamosaurus
(AL-uh-mo-sore-us)
This dinosaur giant was a gentle plant-eater, not a fighter.

Find 1

Gorgosaurus
(GOR-go-sore-us)
Though not as large as T. rex, Gorgosaurus
had a bite that was just as nasty!

Find 5

Leptoceratops
(lep-toe-SAIR-uh-tops)
Leptoceratops, a human-sized dinosaur,
could chew on the toughest plants.

Find 5

Ojoraptorsaurus
(oj-joe-RAP-tuh-sore-us)
Ojoraptorsaurus was a raptor that
looked like a large bird, a small beak.

Saurolophus
(sawr-OL-o-fus)
This duck-billed dino had a bony
spike on the back of its head.

Find 5

Dracorex
(DRAK-o-rex)
This dino was named by Harry
Potter fans as "Dracorex Hogwartsia."

Find 6

19

Xiphactinus
(zee-FACT-in-us)
Xiphactinus, a large, fanged fish, was a strong swimmer that hunted smaller fish.

Find 5

Hybodus
(HY-bo-dus)
A prehistoric fish that looked like a great white shark, but was much smaller.

Find 4

SAVAGE SEAS

The prehistoric oceans were home to large reptiles who were just as dangerous as the dinosaurs on land.

Ichthyosaur
(ICK-thi-o-sore)
This predator looked like a dolphin with large eyes and a jaw full of sharp teeth.

Find 8

Find 3

20

Elasmosaurus
(ee-LAZ-mo-sore-us)
A fish-hunting reptile, it had a neck as long as its body!

Find 5

Kronosaurus
(CROW-no-sore-us)
Kronosaurus was the size of a small whale and a dangerous predator.

Find 7

Archelon
(ar-KEL-on)
Archelon was one of the largest
turtles to have ever lived.

Find 9

Protosphyraena
(pro-toss-fy-RAY-na)
This swordfish-like creature
had lots of razor-sharp teeth.

Find 3

Mosasaurus
(MOSS-a-sore-us)
The largest of the underwater predators,
this lizard was the "T. rex of the seas."

Ammonite
(AM-on-ite)
This squid-like creature grew from
thumb size to the size of a tractor wheel.

Find 10

Find 5

Nautilus
(NAW-tih-lus)
Nautilus, a shelled, tentacled creature,
is still found in today's oceans.

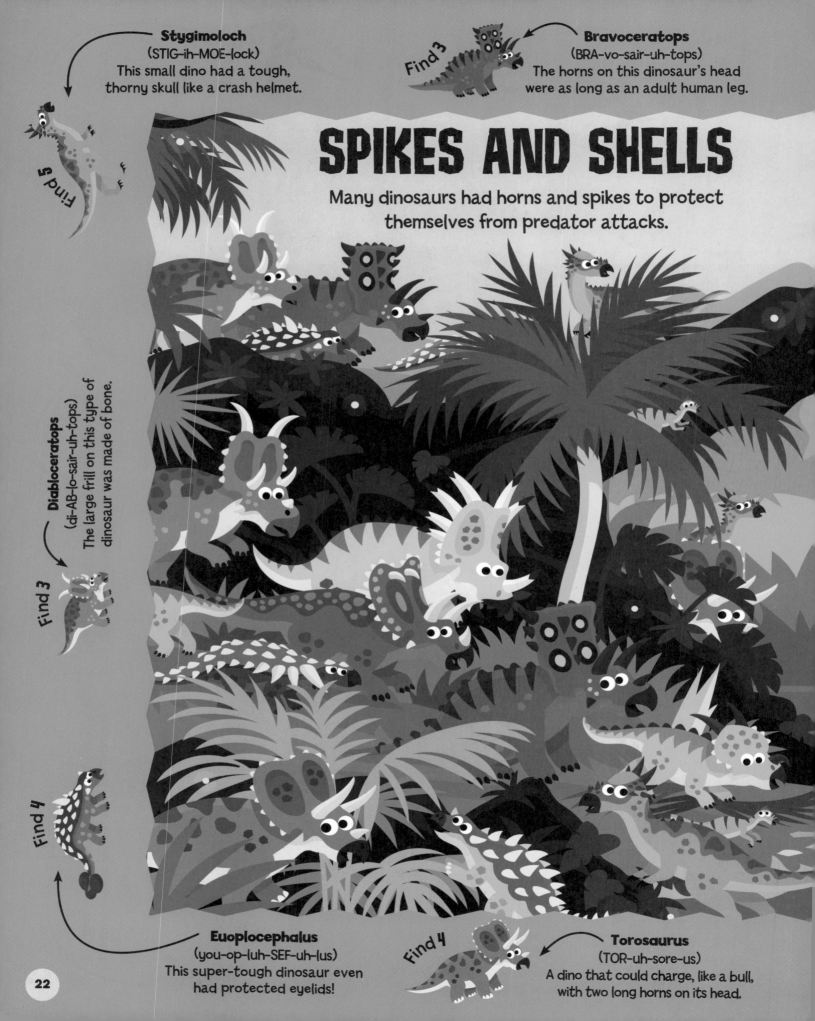

SPIKES AND SHELLS

Many dinosaurs had horns and spikes to protect themselves from predator attacks.

Stygimoloch
(STIG-ih-MOE-lock)
This small dino had a tough, thorny skull like a crash helmet.

Find 5

Find 3

Bravoceratops
(BRA-vo-sair-uh-tops)
The horns on this dinosaur's head were as long as an adult human leg.

Diabloceratops
(di-AB-lo-sair-uh-tops)
The large frill on this type of dinosaur was made of bone.

Find 3

Find 4

Euoplocephalus
(you-op-luh-SEF-uh-lus)
This super-tough dinosaur even had protected eyelids!

Find 4

Torosaurus
(TOR-uh-sore-us)
A dino that could charge, like a bull, with two long horns on its head.

Find 3

Styracosaurus
(stih-RAK-uh-sore-us)
The horned frill around this dino's
head looked like a crown.

Find 3

Ankylosaurus
(ang-KILE-uh-sore-us)
Ankylosaurus, a bus-sized dinosaur, had
a clubbed tail to swing at attackers.

Find 2

Pentaceratops
(PEN-tah-sair-uh-tops)
Pentaceratops had the largest skull
ever found for a land animal.

Edmontonia
(ed-mon-TOE-nia)
This plant-eater put off
predators with its thorny spikes.

Find 4

Einiosaurus
(EYE-nio-sore-us)
An odd-looking dino with a horn
on its nose that pointed down.

Find 4

Mononykus
(mo-NON-i-kus)
These fast-running, geese-like dinosaurs, had very short, clawed arms.

Find 4

Qianzhousaurus
(CHY-an-shoo-sore-us)
This T. rex relative had an unusually long snout.

Find 6

FEATHERS IN THE FOREST

Fossils discovered in China show many dinosaurs had short feathers and even wings on their arms.

Sinosauropteryx
(SY-nuh-saur-OP-te-rix)
Sinosauropteryx was the first feathered dinosaur to be discovered.

Find 4

Find 6

Liaoxiornis
(lee-OW-she-or-nis)
Liaoxiornis, a thumb-sized bird, was one of the smallest of its time.

Find 4

Caudipteryx
(CAW-DIP-teh-rix)
This dinosaur was the size of a goose, with long feathers on its arms.

Find 4

Alxasaurus
(AL-shuh-sore-us)
Though this dinosaur had large
claws, it probably only ate plants.

Find 5

Sinornithosaurus
(Sy-norm-ith-uh-sore-us)
Some scientists think this small dinosaur
had a venomous bite, like a snake.

Find 4

Psittacosaurus
(SIT-uh-ko-sore-us)
Psittacosaurus, a plant-eatingdinosaur,
had horns sticking out of its cheeks.

Nankangia
(nan-CAN-gee-uh)
This emu-sized bird ate
mostly plants.

Find 4

Find 5

Banji
(BAHN-jee)
Banji, a toothless dinosaur, had
a small crest between its eyes.

25

Gastonia
(gas-TOE-nia)
The spikes on this dinosaur's tail
could be used as a weapon.

Deinonychus
(dye-NON-ik-us)
Deinonychus, a fast and feathered
raptor, had long and very sharp claws.

Find 3

LAST DAYS

65 millions years ago, the dinosaurs began
to die out after a large asteroid hit Earth,
causing the sky to darken.

Quetzalcoatlus
(ket-sull-KO-at-lus)
The largest flying animal of all time.
Quetzalcoatlus was the size of a small plane!

Find 3

Find 4

Achelousaurus
(ah-KEL-oo-sore-us)
This dino had a parrot-like beak and
a protective bone frill over its neck.

Find 3

Tenontosaurus
(teh-NON-tuh-sore-us)
Tenontosaurus had a long, heavy
tail that it used for balance.

Find 3

Bravoceratops
(BRA-vo-sair-uh-tops)
Without sunlight plants died, and plant-eaters,
like these Bravoceratops, could not find food.

Find 2

Alamosaurus
(AL-uh-mo-sore-us)
Many of the trees this dino would
have fed on were burnt in wildfires.

Find 8

Orodromeus
(OR-uh-DROM-ee-us)
Orodromeus, a small plant-eater,
may have dug burrows.

Protohadros
(proh-toh-HAD-ros)
"Duck-billed" dinosaurs, like this,
were called hadrosaurs.

Find 3

Find 4

Gryposaurus
(GRYE-pur-sore-us)
This dinosaur had skin covered in
smooth scales the size of fingernails.

27

Hammers or chisels
These are used to cut the fossils from the rock.

Find 5

Paleontologists
(pale-ee-on-tol-oh-jists)
Scientists examine the remains of dinosaurs that they discover in ancient rocks.

Find 9

DINO DIG

Over millions of years, the bones of dinosaurs turned to rocky fossils underground. Scientists carefully dig them up for study.

Claws
These fossils of dinosaur claws are as long as human hands!

Find 4

Find 4

Magnifying glasses
A lens is used to look at the detail on a fossil.

Find 3

Trowels
Trowels are used to dig away soil around the fossilized bones.

Find 6

Brushes
Brushes are used to gently clean dust and soil from a fossil.

Find 3

Tape measures
Experts measure the size and position of the fossils.

Find 4

Buckets
Before a fossil is moved, it is covered in cloth and plaster for protection.

Safety goggles
When hammering rock, goggles protect the scientists' eyes from stone splinters.

Find 5

Thigh bones
These large dinosaur leg bones have been turned into rock over millions of years.

Find 3

ANSWERS

4–5 BEACH BEASTS

- Mastodonsaurus
- Tanystropheus
- Liliensternus
- Plateosaurus
- Gerrothorax
- Thecodontosaurus
- Procompsognathus
- Ruehleia
- Saltopus
- Placochelys

6-7 STAMPEDE!

- Pachyrhinosaurus
- Centrosaurus
- Corythosaurus
- Atrociraptor
- Prosaurolophus
- Albertosaurus
- Euoplocephalus
- Lambeosaurus
- Pachycephalosaurus
- Edmontonia

8-9 GRAZING GIANTS

- Brachiosaurus
- Hesperosaurus
- Apatosaurus
- Dryosaurus
- Allosaurus
- Diplodocus
- Camptosaurus
- Stegosaurus
- Gargoyleosaurus
- Camarasaurus

10–11 SWAMP DWELLERS

- Champsosaurus
- Thescelosaurus
- Albertosaurus
- Adocus
- Puertasaurus
- Ankylosaurus
- Anzu
- Edmontosaurus
- Pteranodon
- Triceratops

12-13 FLOODLAND FEAST

- Eotyrannus
- Hylaeosaurus
- Pelorosaurus
- Baryonyx
- Hypsilophodon
- Polacanthus
- Valdosaurus
- Neovenator
- Iguanodon
- Becklespinax

14-15 BABY BITERS

- Troodon
- Troodon young
- Parasaurolophus
- Dragonflies
- Edmontosaurus
- Triceratops
- Helopanoplia
- Hadrosaurus
- Brachychamsa
- Panoplosaurus

16-17 FLYING HIGH

- Gnathosaurus
- Pterodactylus
- Anurognathus
- Dakosaurus
- Aerodactylus
- Libellulium
- Archaeopteryx
- Dimorphodon
- Rhamphorhynchus
- Scaphognathus

18-19 T. REX TUSSLE

- Tyrannosaurus rex
- Ornithomimus
- Dryptosaurus
- Thescelosaurus
- Alamosaurus
- Dracorex
- Saurolophus
- Ojoraptorsaurus
- Leptocerotops
- Gorgosaurus

20–21 SAVAGE SEAS

- Hybodus
- Xiphactinus
- Ichthyosaur
- Elasmosaurus
- Kronosaurus
- Nautilus
- Ammonite
- Mosasaurus
- Protosphyraena
- Archelon

22–23 SPIKES AND SHELLS

- Bravoceratops
- Stygimoloch
- Diabloceratops
- Euoplocephalus
- Torosaurus
- Einiosaurus
- Edmontonia
- Pentaceratops
- Ankylosaurus
- Styracosaurus

24–25 FEATHERS IN THE FOREST

- Qianzhousaurus
- Mononykus
- Sinosauropteryx
- Liaoxiornis
- Caudipteryx
- Banji
- Nankangia
- Psittacosaurus
- Sinornithosaurus
- Alxasaurus

26–27 LAST DAYS

- Deinonychus
- Gastonia
- Quetzalcoatlus
- Achelousaurus
- Tenontosaurus
- Gryposaurus
- Protohadros
- Orodromeus
- Alamosaurus
- Bravoceratops

28–29 DINO DIG

- Palaeontologists
- Hammers or chisels
- Claws
- Magnifying glasses
- Trowels
- Thigh bones
- Safety goggles
- Buckets
- Tape measures
- Brushes